Dealing with death in hospital

PROCEDURES FOR MANAGERS AND STAFF

Dealing with death in hospital

PROCEDURES FOR MANAGERS AND STAFF

Susan Hughes and Alix Henley

Department of Public Health,
Bloomsbury Health Authority

King Edward's Hospital Fund for London

© King's Edward's Hospital Fund for London 1990
Typeset by Tradespools Ltd
Printed and bound in England by Hollen Street Press
Distributed for the King's Fund by Bailey Distribution Ltd

ISBN 1 85551 057 X

King's Fund Publishing Office
14 Palace Court
London W2 4HT

Contents

Appendices

Foreword

Hospital managers are under such pressure these days that they may allow some of the more basic administrative tasks to be undertaken by inexperienced junior staff. This book reminds us that we are often judged by the way we perform these tasks.

Dealing with death in hospital is just another event for most staff and its ordinariness may lead to casualness. But for relatives and friends the death may be devastating. For some of them, it will be their first experience of death and they will need not only clear advice but also sympathy to help them with their grieving.

The book provides managers and their administrative staff with a systematic checklist for each stage in the handling of a death. Equally important is the Glossary of terms and specific situations which tell the reader what to do when faced with some of the more complicated issues such as the removal of organs or observing religious differences.

It is now generally recognised that managers have an ethical component to their work. Handling the arrangements following a death requires respect for the individual, respect for privacy and a duty to obtain appropriate consent; these are all fundamental criteria of sound ethical practice.

Andrew Wall
Bath Health District

Acknowledgements

We should like to thank all the people, both inside and outside Bloomsbury Health Authority, who have commented on and improved this book, in particular Dr June Crown, Director of Public Health, Bloomsbury Health Authority. We are also indebted to Stephen Bolton, Chief Clerk, Faculty Office of the Archbishop of Canterbury; Ita Catchpole, Patient Services' Officer, University College Hospital; Kay Ford, Regional Transplant Coordinator, North East Thames Regional Health Authority; Dr Gillian Gau, Queen Charlotte's Hospital; Mr A Goonewardene, Polytechnic of North London; Susan Lazarus, Operational Services Manager, Goodmayes Hospital; Paddy Lyons, Patient Services' Officer, The Middlesex Hospital; Myc Riggulsford, United Kingdom Transplant Service; Sylvia Ritten, Director, Moorfields Eye Bank; Norman Stephens, Secretary, Institute of Population Registration; Fred Adelmann and Bernard and Rebecca Hughes. Any errors or faults that have crept into the text despite their comments and suggestions are entirely our own responsibility.

1 Introduction

When a patient dies in hospital, his or her relatives* have to carry out various practical tasks, such as collecting property and collecting the doctor's certificate to take to the registrar. The person in the hospital responsible for dealing with relatives on most of these matters may have a title such as bereavement officer, patient affairs officer or relatives' officer. For convenience, we have used bereavement officer throughout this book.

For relatives, dealing with practical matters immediately after someone has died can be extremely distressing. A kind, well-organised, well-informed bereavement officer, who can guide and support them through the necessary procedures, is of tremendous value.

This book provides bereavement officers and other hospital staff with a comprehensive guide to the legal and administrative requirements which surround the death of a person in hospital and with advice on offering assistance and support to bereaved relatives.

*Throughout this book 'relatives' may include close friends.

2 The task of hospital management

Many complaints from relatives arise from inadequate hospital procedures in the period following a death. Relatives often feel pushed hither and thither, unimportant, and even a hindrance. The staff they deal with do not always seem to know what they should be doing. Essential communication between staff is often poor. To ensure good, well-coordinated care it is strongly recommended that one person has overall responsibility for dealing with relatives in hospital after a death. It is important that she* has sufficient authority to ensure that everything at this time is dealt with to a high standard.

THE BEREAVEMENT OFFICER'S ROLE

Her main tasks are:

* To keep clear accurate records relating to each death in the hospital and to prepare the paperwork for each interview.

* To check and hand over any property and valuables to the relatives.

* To give the relatives the signed certificate they need to register the death, and to explain what they need to do next.

* If a death is referred to the coroner, to explain the main implications of this to relatives.

* To answer relatives' questions about any other necessary procedures.

*We have used 'she' and 'her' for the bereavement officer throughout, although we recognise that many are men. Nurses are referred to as 'she' and doctors as 'he'.

- To ensure, as far as possible, that relatives leave the hospital satisfied with the care and attention that they have received.

Also:

- To ensure that there is a clear, written statement available and known to all relevant staff of the procedures to be followed after a patient dies, setting out administrative, medical, nursing and other responsibilities, and emphasising the prime importance of consideration and support for the bereaved relatives. There must also be clear statements for procedures to be followed at weekends and outside normal working hours.

- To inform other appropriate departments and agencies of deaths.

- To ensure that the mortuary chapel and the way there are well maintained and that relatives who view bodies at the hospital are well cared for.

- To attempt to trace a person's next of kin if necessary.

- To register a death if there are no relatives who can do so.

- To arrange funerals in certain circumstances.

- To receive cremation fees from funeral directors and pass them on to the hospital cashier.

- To deal with any unclaimed property.

- To ensure, through formal training or other means, that all other relevant hospital staff know what the bereavement officer does and how to contact her, and that they know and carry out their own responsibilities following a death.

Note: The rules affecting the registration of births and deaths may change when an opportunity arises to legislate on the proposals in the white paper *Registration: proposals for change.*

3 The bereavement officer's room

The office should be attractive and well maintained. There should be a pleasant adjoining room where relatives can wait in private. The two rooms should have their own doors as well as a shared door so that relatives leaving the office do not have to walk past other people waiting to see her. The office should be sited away from the wards and other busy areas to ensure privacy and a calm atmosphere. There should also be generous cupboard space so that property awaiting collection can be stored out of sight.

If possible the bereavement officer should have a direct telephone line so that relatives, funeral directors, coroners' officers and others can all contact her easily. When she is seeing relatives the telephone should be routed through a secretary who can take messages. Relatives should be offered the free use of the telephone for urgent outside calls.

Tea, coffee and biscuits should be provided free in the waiting room. There should also be a stock of leaflets for relatives to look at while they wait and to take away, about, for example, organising a funeral, social security benefits, and counselling and support services for the bereaved.

OPENING TIMES

The opening times of the office should be known to hospital staff and stated on the door.

It is usually best to have an appointment system so that relatives do not have to queue to see the bereavement officer. Appointment times should take into account the time needed to get to the registrar's office so that relatives can go on to register the death on the same day if they wish. The appointment book should be kept with the officer or her secretary during office hours. Outside normal working hours, the appointment book should be kept at the porter's desk in the front hall or with the senior nurse on duty.

ARRANGEMENTS OUTSIDE NORMAL WORKING HOURS

Many of the problems relatives experience in hospitals following a death arise outside normal working hours. In hospitals with a large number of deaths, the bereavement officer should be present to see relatives and deal with any problems on weekend mornings. At other times, or where this is not possible, she should be on call or should have trained the on-call manager or whoever is responsible to provide an adequate service.

4 Before the interview

ARRANGING FOR RELATIVES TO SEE THE BEREAVEMENT OFFICER

When a patient has died on a ward, a nurse should explain to relatives that they (or someone in their place) will need to come back to the hospital at a convenient time to collect the necessary certificate and any property. (In some cases property may be collected from the ward by the relatives either straight away or the next day.)

The nurse should find out when the relatives would like to see the bereavement officer, usually on the next working day. She should give them an appointment card with the officer's name and telephone number so that they can change the appointment if they wish. All nursing staff must know what to tell relatives and how to make an appointment.

In some hospitals nursing staff also give relatives a small leaflet with important information and contact numbers before they leave the ward (see Appendix A for an example).

A nurse should inform the bereavement officer in advance if she is likely to need an interpreter, and if there is anything else she needs to be aware of before the interview.

COMPLETING THE HOSPITAL REGISTERS

Good record keeping is essential for efficiency now and so that information can be found easily if it is needed later.

The bereavement officer should enter each death in two hospital registers: in the first, the deaths should be entered in chronological order as they occur (see Appendix B); in the second (which should be indexed) the deaths should be entered alphabetically by surname, with other essential information to enable cross-referencing to the first register in case there are enquiries about the death or the funeral arrangements at a later date (see Appendix C).

ASSEMBLING PAPERS AND PROPERTY

The bereavement officer must have all the necessary papers and property ready before she sees the relatives. She can then concentrate fully on the relatives and their needs during the interview.

She will need:

1. The patient's medical record from the ward so that she can complete the hospital registers, call the appropriate doctor, and find out essential information – about the patient's religion, for example.

2. The medical cause of death certificate, signed by the appropriate doctor, to give to the relatives to take to the registrar.

3. A release slip (or authorisation slip) authorising the hospital mortuary staff to release the body to the funeral director (see Appendix D). The relatives need to sign this and give it to the funeral director.

4. The patient's property, including personal possessions, clothing, valuables, jewellery, and money (collected from the ward and hospital safes) to give to the relatives.

5. The property sheet, completed when the patient was admitted to hospital and kept by the hospital

cashier. The relatives must sign this to confirm that they have received the items listed on it.

6. An indemnity form for the relatives to sign indemnifying the health authority against future claims by other people on any valuables (see Appendix E).

7. A consent form for a hospital post mortem, if required, which the relatives sign if they consent. Also the telephone or bleep number of the doctor who will be asking the relatives for their consent, so that he can be contacted at the right time.

8. A funeral expenses form, in case it is required (see Appendix F and **Funeral expenses – help with**, page 33).

The bereavement officer should also keep a stock of important information to give to relatives as needed:

9. A list of local funeral directors, with names and addresses.

10. Details of how to get to the registrar's office by public transport, parking facilities, a map, office opening hours, telephone number, and a list of the information the relatives will need to provide to register the death (see **Registering the death**, page 47).

11. Information about the coroner's office, the address, office telephone number, how to get there by public transport, parking facilities, a map, details of opening hours on weekdays, weekends and public holidays, and telephone numbers out of normal working hours (see **Coroner**, page 19).

12. The address, telephone number and other essential details of the local social security office.

13. Copies of Department of Social Security (DSS) leaflets D49 and FB29.

14. Leaflets about local counselling and bereavement services and local national support groups.

5 Seeing the relatives

Many relatives are distressed during the interview and find it difficult to take in or remember what they are told. Time and patience are needed. It is most important that relatives feel that they are being treated with courtesy and respect and that they feel able to ask questions, seek explanations and discuss funeral arrangements if they wish. The bereavement officer has a crucial role in providing sympathetic support and practical help at this time.

During the interview, only the papers concerning the death she is discussing should be visible. The relatives should feel that they are her sole concern while they are with her.

During the interview the bereavement officer should:

- Welcome the relatives, make them as comfortable as possible and explain her role.

- Tactfully establish the exact relationship of the people to whom she is speaking with the deceased patient. This is particularly important because property is to be handed over.

- Give the relatives a signed copy of the medical cause of death certificate to give to the registrar. Tell them that they must register the death at the local registrar's office within five days of the date of death; explain how to register the death (see **Registering the death**, page 47) and what information they will need to give the registrar; tell them how to get there and give them a map. Many relatives will never have registered a death before.

- If it seems appropriate, check whether the relatives are likely to want a cremation, explaining that this information is required in order to get the necessary forms signed at the hospital. If the relatives have not yet decided, or it is felt that it would be insensitive to ask at this time, the funeral director can inform her later (see **Cremation**, page 24).

- Hand over any property and valuables and receive a signed indemnity form and property sheet.

- Give the relatives a release slip (or authorisation slip – see page 49) to sign and give to the funeral director.

- If necessary, call a doctor to ask the relatives if they will consent to a post mortem.

- Offer to arrange an appointment for the relatives to see the doctors and/or nurses involved in the care of the patient to discuss any concerns or questions they may have about the illness or the death. This is very important.

- If appropriate, ask whether the relatives would like to speak to the hospital chaplain.

- If appropriate and possible, ask if a relative on their own would like a volunteer to go with them to register the death.

- Check that the relatives know that they can view the patient's body before it is moved to the funeral director's and explain how to arrange this.

- Finally check that the relatives know what they need to do after they leave her office and whether they have any other questions.

Most interviews will require at least 25 minutes. This is time well spent for everyone concerned. Pressure to hurry and lack of consideration at this stage may lead to justifiable complaints by relatives later.

6 After the interview

INFORMING OTHER HOSPITAL DEPARTMENTS OF THE DEATH

Considerable distress can be caused to relatives if, some time after the death, a letter confirming an outpatient appointment is received or an ambulance calls. Bereavement officers, nurses and doctors are each responsible for informing various people and departments that a death has occurred. It is most important that each person knows whom they must inform and that they do it as soon as possible.

The bereavement officer should normally inform:

the admissions' office
the outpatients' department
the chaplain's office
the voluntary services' department
surgical appliances
the transport department
the social work department
the private patient's office, if there is one.

In some hospitals she also informs the patient's general practitioner although this is really the responsibility of the medical team. A doctor should telephone the patient's GP on the day of the death and follow this up with a full letter as soon as possible. However, in many cases both the phone call and the doctor's letter are delayed. This can cause serious problems with relatives since they usually assume that the GP will have been informed at once.

Appendix G contains a sample letter which the bereavement officer can get the doctor to sign as a back up when he signs the medical cause of death certificate. This letter should be sent by first class post the same day.

Glossary of terms and specific situations

Accident and emergency department

The bereavement officer's role in dealing with a death that has occurred in an accident and emergency (A & E) department is much as normal but there may be additional complications because the death is likely to have been completely unexpected and possibly violent.

The officer should collect all property, clothing and so on (provided it is not wanted by the police) from the A & E department well before the relatives are due to arrive. She must also find out something about the circumstances of the death so that she can respond sensitively to the relatives, who are likely to be particularly shocked. (In some hospitals the A & E nursing staff who are looking after the relatives also give them any property. In this case, the bereavement officer must check that they know exactly what to do and what other information to give the relatives.)

Most deaths that occur in A & E will be referred to the coroner. Relatives will need advice and guidance on what this is likely to mean and what they should do. (See **Coroner**, page 19.)

If the relatives wish to view the body in the viewing chapel, it is particularly important to make sure that a trained nurse checks that the body is ready for viewing and accompanies them to the chapel. (See also **Viewing the body**, page 54.)

All press enquiries about a death in A & E must be forwarded to a designated manager or to the bereavement officer. A & E staff and other staff should not normally give information to the press but should brief the designated person regularly and at the beginning of each working day. (See **Suggested reading**, page 73.)

Acting for the next of kin

If the relatives are too old or frail to visit the hospital to collect the doctor's certificate and the property, the bereavement officer should offer to register the death for them.

She should register the death as normal, giving the hospital as the place of death and signing the register as 'the occupier'. If the relatives would also like her to arrange the funeral, she should ask them to write formally to her saying this and, if appropriate, asking her to pay for it from the deceased person's estate. If there is no estate, and the relatives are unable or unwilling to pay, see **Funeral expenses – help with,** page 33. (See also **Funerals – arranged by the hospital,** page 30.)

If a hospital post mortem is wanted, the relative must give written consent (see **Post mortem – hospital,** page 43). Send a standard consent form with a stamped addressed envelope, and a covering letter requesting a post mortem from the doctor.

Keep the relatives informed of any complications – for example, a coroner's post mortem.

Authorisation slip

see **Release slip** page 49.

Baptism in hospital

In the Church of England, Church in Wales and Roman Catholic Church, anyone can legitimately perform a baptismal service, whatever their beliefs.

For the baptism to be valid, the person must pour water over the patient's head, saying at the same time: 'I baptise thee in the name of the Father, the Son and the Holy Spirit'. It is not necessary to give the patient a name during this ceremony.

In an emergency, bleep the appropriate chaplain and tell him where the baptism is needed and how urgent it is. If he cannot get there in time, anyone else may baptise the patient as outlined above. The chaplain will enter the baptism in the baptismal register, usually kept in the neonatal or maternity unit, and also in the parish register.

If the patient recovers, he or she can receive a full baptism later.

Buddhist patients and families   Most Buddhists prefer cremation, but this is a matter of personal choice. Cremation is normally carried out between three and seven days after the death.

There is no religious objection to organ donation or post mortems.

Burial order   Issued by the coroner to relatives after an inquest. (See **Coroner's inquest**, page 20.)

Certificate for burial or cremation   Also known as the green form, it is given by the registrar to the relatives once they have registered the death. They give it to their funeral director to permit the burial or cremation to go ahead. If the death is of a newborn baby and the hospital is arranging the funeral, the parents should give the form to the bereavement officer: see **Neonatal death**, page 40.

Certificate for burial or cremation (stillbirth)   This is given to the parents of a stillborn baby when they register the birth to permit the burial or to allow them to apply for a cremation. The parents should give it to whoever is arranging the funeral – that is, the funeral director or the bereavement officer. (See **Stillbirth**, page 50.)

Certificate of registration of death	Given by the registrar to the relatives, it is usually known as the death certificate. (See also **Registering the death**, page 47.)
Chaplain	If the medical records indicate that a chaplain has been involved with the patient or the relatives, the bereavement officer should offer the relatives the opportunity to see him. Church of England chaplains can often help contact appropriate people to visit or perform last rites for people of different faiths.
Christian patients and families	(The following applies to most Christian groups, although there may be some variation among the minority Christian groups in Britain.) There is no doctrinal preference for either burial or cremation. Older people, particularly Roman Catholics, may prefer burial. Some Christian groups whose families originated in hot climates strongly prefer to hold the funeral as soon as possible. There is no teaching against organ donation. In fact organ donation may be encouraged as an act of charity, giving life to another There is no teaching against post mortems provided the body is treated with respect. (See also **Jehovah's Witness patients and families**, page 34.)
Contract funeral	See **Funeral – arranged by the hospital**, page 30.

Coroner

The doctor who verifies a death must report it to the coroner if:

- the death was sudden;
- the cause is unknown;
- the death was due to a medical error;
- the death was due to drugs;
- no doctor attended the patient in his/her last illness;
- a doctor responsible for the care of the patient did not see him/her within 14 days before his/her death;
- the death occurred during or within 24 hours of surgery;
- the death occurred while the patient was under anaesthetic or within 24 hours of coming round from an anaesthetic;
- the death may have been caused by industrial disease or injury;
- the death may have been caused by violence, neglect, poisoning or abortion.

If the doctor is not sure whether to report a death he should always telephone the coroner as soon as possible to discuss the case.

If the death is reported to the coroner, the doctor who verifies the death does not always sign the medical cause of death certificate. He should tell the relatives that the death has been reported to the coroner and why, and also that this will not necessarily mean a post mortem or an inquest. If the coroner does carry out a post mortem this should not normally delay funeral arrangements. (See also **Coroner's post mortem**, page 22.)

If a death is reported to the coroner and becomes a coroner's case the relatives do not register the death immediately in the normal way. They should be encouraged to contact the coroner's office (where someone is on call 24 hours a day) as soon as possible for more information. The bereavement officer should give the relatives the coroner's address and telephone number and a map of how to get there. However, the relatives can begin to make arrangements with the funeral director of their choice.

Unless he decides to hold an inquest, the coroner, once certain of the cause of death, normally sends a form (form 100) to the registrar to register the death. The registrar informs the relatives.

Coroners are always happy to give advice to bereavement officers if any questions arise.

Coroner's inquest   The coroner must hold an inquest whenever there is reason to suspect that the death was due to violence or any unnatural cause – for example, suicide, road accident, violence. The coroner is also likely to hold an inquest whenever allegations of inadequate or improper treatment or care are made against a doctor or a hospital. The legal purpose of an inquest is to ascertain the name of the deceased person, how, when and where the death occurred, and the details needed to register the death.

Inquests may also be beneficial if they either exonerate the person or institution concerned or, if the allegations are proved, they lead to problems being remedied. Inquests can also draw the attention of the public to dangers.

If the coroner decides that a formal inquest is

necessary he will normally open it as soon as possible (usually within a few days) and adjourn it immediately so that he can issue the burial order or cremation form to enable the relatives to go ahead with the funeral. The funeral cannot take place until this is done. The burial order contains two parts: B, which the relatives give to the funeral director; and C, which they must hand to the registrar within 96 hours. If the body is to be cremated, the coroner will give a copy of form E to the relatives once the inquest is open. If the relatives are not available, the coroner will issue the appropriate form directly to the funeral director. The doctors do not receive cremation fees in a coroner's case.

Once the inquest is over the coroner will send a certificate to the registrar to enable him to register the death. (Occasionally he will send it via the next of kin or, if the next of kin have not been traced, to the hospital administrator. Relatives can then apply, in person or in writing, to the registrar for copies of the death certificate and will be charged the normal fee per copy. (See **Registering the death**, page 47.)

Inquests are held in a courtroom attached to the coroner's office. Unlike a trial, there are no prosecutors or defendants. The coroner questions each witness. Other interested parties may also question witnesses if the coroner gives permission. The family of the dead person, health service staff who are to be called as witnesses, trades unions, employers and insurance companies may all be legally represented. Legal Aid cannot be obtained for inquests.

Inquests are public and there are no reporting restrictions except on publishing the names of minors.

If it is necessary for the bereavement officer to attend the inquest as an observer, she should take careful notes of the proceedings, including the findings of the pathologist and the coroner's conclusions.

Coroner's inquest – appeal

It is not possible to appeal against the coroner's conclusion. However, people can question his conclusion on grounds of fraud, error of law, bias, exceeding his powers, or insufficient evidence, through a judicial review before the divisional court. A judge will then review the evidence and decide whether to order a fresh inquest or to quash the application.

Coroner's inquest – jury

Occasionally a coroner's inquest is held with a jury. Juries are required if the death occurred in prison, police custody, was caused by a police officer or was the result of an industrial accident. A jury inquest may also be held if a family is dissatisfied with a coroner's original conclusion and he agrees to hold another inquest.

Coroner's post mortem

A coroner may order a post mortem if he is unsure of the cause of death. Coroner's post mortems are normally carried out by the consultant histopathologist at the local general hospital. If foul play is suspected or extensive litigation is likely, the post mortem will be carried out by a forensic pathologist, usually in the public mortuary. A coroner's post mortem does not normally delay the funeral.

If the next of kin wish to object to a coroner's post mortem for any reason, they should be advised to contact the coroner immediately, using the hospital telephone if they wish, since coroner's post mortems are usually done as soon as possible. The coroner or one of his officers can be contacted 24 hours a day.

However, while doing all you can to give practical help it is important not to assume the role of relatives' advocate in making the objection. The hospital and its employees must by law act as agents of the coroner and follow his instructions.

If the coroner feels that it is necessary for legal reasons to carry out a post mortem, he has the right to do so, unless the relatives apply successfully to the high court to stop him. (*R v Bristol Coroner ex p Kerr 1974*).

If the coroner carries out a post mortem but not an inquest he will give the relatives a form – form 100 – with which to register the death. (This is the equivalent of the medical cause of death certificate normally issued by the hospital.) The registrar will then give the relatives a death certificate and a certificate for burial or cremation. (See also **Coroner's inquest**, page 20.)

The Coroner does not usually give the next of kin a copy of the post mortem report, but may sometimes send one to the deceased patient's consultant. This should be placed with the patient's medical records. The bereavement officer should offer the relatives an opportunity to discuss the post mortem findings and their concerns with the relevant consultant or suggest that they speak to their general practitioner.

Counselling and support

All staff who deal with dying patients or bereaved relatives may require counselling and support. Basic support should be provided through open and easy access to line managers. In addition, the bereavement officer should have easy access to an appropriate trained professional who is not part of her line management – for example, psychologist, counsellor, chaplain – to discuss the strains of the work in general, and any particularly difficult situations.

Cremation   A body cannot be cremated until the death has been
legally verified and the appropriate forms completed
by two qualified doctors, the cause of death has been
clearly stated, the death has been registered, and a
certificate of burial or cremation (green form) has
been obtained from the registrar (or, in a coroner's
case, a cremation form).

Because of the legal procedures involved and
crematorium regulations (some crematoria require
the necessary papers 48 hours in advance of the pro-
posed cremation date), it can take several days to
organise a cremation even after the medical forms
have been signed at the hospital. For this reason, it is
most important to get all the relevant hospital forms
signed as soon as possible, so that the funeral is not
delayed and the relatives are not further distressed.

During her interview the bereavement officer
should try to find out sensitively whether the relatives want a burial or a cremation. If they have not
yet decided, she should ask them to let her know as
soon as they do and explain why.

There are four statutory parts to a cremation form,
known as forms A, B, C and F. Form B must be completed by a doctor who attended the deceased person
during his or her last illness. He must see the body
before filling in the form. If no doctor has seen the
patient in the previous 14 days the death must be
reported to the coroner.

Form C, on the same piece of paper, is the confir-
matory medical certificate which must be completed
by a doctor who has been fully registered as a medical
practitioner with the General Medical Council in the
UK for at least five years. This doctor must not be
related to the deceased patient nor to the doctor who
completed form B. He must also see the body before
signing the form.

Form A is an application for cremation and must be completed by the executor or next-of-kin and countersigned by a householder who knows him/her personally. This is usually organised by the funeral director.

Once all the papers are signed, the funeral director sends them to the medical referee at the crematorium. If he is satisfied, he completes form F and authorises the cremation. (See also **Stillbirth**, page 50.)

Cremation fees

Except in the case of a stillbirth (see page 50), a fee is paid to each doctor who signs the cremation form. The funeral director normally collects the fees from the relatives as part of his bill, and passes them back to the bereavement officer. She gives the funeral director a receipt and hands the money to the hospital cashier, receiving a receipt in turn. The hospital cashier then pays the doctors. The doctors' fee is set anually by the British Medical Association which notifies regional medical officers of the new charges.

Any arrangements which the bereavement officer makes for handling the money should be reviewed regularly by the health authority's auditors. She should consult the auditors if she is not happy with the existing arrangements.

Cremation form

See **Cremation** (page 24) and **Coroner's inquest** (page 20).

Death certificate

See **Certificate of registration of death** (page 18) and **Registering the death** (page 47).

Death grant   This no longer exists. Some people can get help with
                           funeral expenses. (See **Funeral expenses – help
                           with**, page 33.)

Donating a body for   This is governed by the 1984 Anatomy Act. A body
medical research   can only be donated for medical research if the
                           deceased person stated this as their wish during their
                           last illness in the presence of two witnesses or gave
                           their consent in writing *and* the surviving spouse or
                           other next of kin or other close surviving relatives do
                           not object. A body cannot be donated for medical
                           research if the death has been reported to the cor-
                           oner, if the death was due to cancer, AIDS or another
                           infectious disease, or if the body has undergone a
                           post mortem or had any organ removed.

                           If all these conditions are met the bereavement
                           officer should organise the donation. Contact the
                           department of morbid anatomy or histopathology at
                           your nearest medical school or (in the south of
                           England only) the London Anatomy Office, Rocke-
                           feller Building, University College, University Street,
                           London WC1E 6JJ (071-387 7850). They will decide
                           whether the body is suitable, make all the necessary
                           arrangements, and will advise on any problems.

                           For general advice about the donation of bodies for
                           medical research contact HM Inspector of Anatomy,
                           Department of Health, Eileen House, 80–94
                           Newington Causeway, London SE1 (071-703 6380,
                           ext 3743) or outside normal working hours, the
                           Department of Health (071-407 5522).

                           The institution that receives the body is respon-
                           sible for removing it from the hospital and for arrang-
                           ing and paying for a funeral of the appropriate
                           denomination and for burial or cremation, unless the
                           relatives want to make their own arrangements.

Once the institution accepts the body they will ask the relatives whether they want a private funeral, a burial or cremation, whether they wish to be notified and to attend, whether they want the ashes if the body is cremated and whether they have any other special instructions. They do not put up individual headstones, although the relatives can organise this. The body may be ready for burial or cremation as long as three years after the death, though it is more usually one or two years.

The relatives should register the death in the usual way and send the certificate for burial or cremation (green form) which the registrar gives to the London Anatomy Office or to the appropriate medical school.

After the formalities have been completed the receiving institution will invite the relatives to an annual interdenominational service of thanksgiving.

Donating corneas

Donated corneas can restore sight in patients with certain conditions. The colour of the eyes, and the sex, race, blood group and tissue type of the donor do not matter in cornea donation. Only a few conditions, such as eye surgery in the past, eye infections and diseases, septicaemia, serum hepatitis, and AIDS preclude cornea donation. There is no upper age limit. Removing corneas is quick and easy and does not alter the appearance of the donor's face. The corneas should ideally be removed within six hours of the death but can be removed up to 24 hours after the death if the body has been refrigerated.

As with other organ donations (see below) the relatives must give their consent, verbally or in writing. Cornea donation should not delay the funeral.

Cornea donation is organised in London by the

Moorfields Eye Hospital Eye Bank. The Eye Bank can be contacted 24 hours a day to arrange donation or for information or advice (telephone 071-253 1199, outside normal working hours 071-253 3411). They usually send someone to remove the corneas and, if the relatives wish, will send them a letter acknowledging their gift and giving a limited amount of information about the recipient.

Outside London contact your regional transplant coordinator, the hospital's ophthalmology department, or the United Kingdom Transplant Service (24 hour telephone line, 0272 507777, ask for UKTS) for advice and help in making arrangements.

Donating organs

This is governed by the Anatomy Act 1984 and parts of the Human Tissue Act 1961. Organs can only be donated if the person who legally owns the body agrees (normally the next of kin but, if they are not available, the officer appointed by the health authority) and there is no reason to believe that the deceased person would have objected and there is no objection from a surviving spouse or other close relative. If the deceased person is under 18 years of age, consent can only be given by parents or guardians.

Even if the deceased person stated, either verbally or in writing, that his or her organs should be used for donation, the organs cannot be donated if the surviving spouse or other next of kin or another close surviving relative objects. The main consideration must be the peace of mind of the relatives.

Organ donation should not disfigure the body in any way and should not delay the funeral. The relatives register the death in the normal way.

Certain medical conditions or circumstances preclude organ donation. For example, if the person had cancer, AIDS, serum hepatitis or some other infectious disease.

Asking relatives if they will consent to organ donation is an extremely sensitive task. All staff can contact the regional transplant coordinator for help and guidance with this. The regional transplant coordinator is always happy to speak to the relatives themselves, and will organise the donation if consent is given. (See also *Cadaveric organs for transplantation: a code of practice, including the diagnosis of brain death*, HMSO 1983.)

Managers should also ensure that their hospital, if appropriate, has explicit procedures for identifying potential organ donors and for notifying the appropriate transplant coordinator or unit. See HC(88)63, *Provision of donor organs for transplantation*.

Organ donation can attract a good deal of press interest. All the details of organ donors and recipients should normally be kept confidential. The relatives' wishes regarding publicity should be recorded in the case notes.

Donating organs – coroner's cases

If the death is likely to be referred to the coroner he must give his consent to the organ donation. However, he is only likely to refuse consent if 'he is aware that there may be later criminal proceedings in which the organ may be required as evidence, if he believes that the removal of an organ might impede his own further enquiries, or if he has reason to believe that a defect in the organ itself was the cause, or contributory cause, of death' (Home Office circular no 65/1977, *Transplant surgery*). Organs cannot be donated if homicide is suspected.

**Donating organs –
no next of kin**

The health authority should nominate a responsible officer as having the power to consent to organ donation in cases where the deceased person's next of kin are not available. The responsible officer can give her consent providing she is satisfied that the deceased person and any surviving relatives who can be contacted had or have no objection. However, it is rare for organs to be donated under such circumstances, both because there is a danger that if the next of kin is ever contacted he or she may be unhappy that organs have been donated and, nowadays, because of concern about AIDS.

**Donating organs –
the transplant team**

If several organs are to be donated, a team of 12 or 13 people will come to the hospital. The regional transplant coordinator will contact the bereavement officer or other appropriate manager so that security and portering staff can be given the details. Sometimes a landing site may need to be marked out for a helicopter. Notify the local fire brigade and police in case of an accident. Arrange refreshments for the transplant team.

Form 100

In coroner's cases only this form is given to the relatives by the coroner (unless there is to be an inquest) so that they can register the death.

**Funeral – arranged
by the hospital**

Under the provisions of HM(72)41, hospitals can arrange and, if necessary, pay for a contract funeral:

* if there is no known next of kin;

* if the next of kin cannot pay for a funeral themselves but cannot get assistance from the Social

Fund (see also **Funeral expenses – help with,** page 33);

- for a stillborn baby, provided the parents wish it (see **Stillbirth**, page 50);
- if the death is that of a baby aged less than 28 days, provided the parents wish it. (See **Neonatal death,** page 40.)

All reasonable funeral expenses are a first charge on the deceased person's estate. Any cash belonging to the deceased person held by the hospital may be used to pay for the funeral provided the procedures laid down by the DHA's auditors are followed. If the hospital has the deceased person's pension book, the cashier should write to the Department of Social Security to claim money for funeral expenses on behalf of the health authority.

The hospital should pay any outstanding funeral costs out of the funeral expenses budget. Some hospitals also pay for flowers and transport for mourners from the hospital.

The type of funeral should be decided on the basis of any available information about the deceased patient's religion or family background. If necessary, contact a representative of the appropriate faith to find out whether there is a religious preference for burial or cremation. Some religious organisations will organise a funeral and burial or cremation for a member of their faith for an agreed fee. Otherwise, use the funeral director with whom the hospital already has a contract. (See also **Funeral directors,** page 32.)

The bereavement officer should keep a detailed file on all aspects of the funeral. Record the deceased person's full name, age, and date of birth, their last known address, their date, place and cause of death, the names of the medical staff involved, the date and type of funeral, the location of the grave, who arranged the funeral, the name and address of the funeral director, any religious organisation involved, and any other essential details. Also, if there are no next of kin, record details of attempts to trace relatives, organisations informed of the death, and details of any estate and how it was wound up. All this will be important if a relative turns up later. The file should be kept for at least eight years.

If the next of kin refuse to pay for a funeral but there is reason to believe that they can afford it (see HM(72)41) the bereavement officer should ask the local authority to arrange a burial or cremation under the provisions of the Public Health (Control of Disease) Act 1984 (S46(1)).

In the case of a stillborn baby the hospital should pay if the parents wish them to arrange the funeral. (See **Stillbirth**, page 50.)

Funeral directors

Funeral directors are an invaluable source of help and relatives should be encouraged to contact them as soon as possible for advice on funeral arrangements and on dealing with any complications. The bereavement officer can also use them as an important source of (anonymous) regular feedback on how well relatives feel that they are treated by hospital staff.

Funeral directors are responsible for ensuring that cremation fees are handed over to the bereavement officer. They are also responsible for collecting a body from the hospital mortuary before the funeral.

The hospital will have a contract with a local funeral director, arranged through the supplies department, for carrying out hospital funerals. The bereavement officer should attend some of these funerals to ensure that the standard of care is acceptable.

Funeral expenses – help with

Relatives should be told that if they or their partner get income support, family credit, or housing benefit (rent rebate, rent allowance or community charge rebate) they may be able to get money towards the cost of the funeral. They should get form SF200 (which has an explanatory leaflet attached) from the administrator or from their local DSS office, or telephone freeline social security 0800 666 555, or contact their local citizen's advice bureau. Details about the money available and how to get it are also given in leaflets DSS D49 and FB29.

If the parents of a stillborn baby accept the hospital's offer to arrange the funeral the hospital should pay. (See also **Stillbirth**, page 50.)

Green form

See **Certificate of burial or cremation**, page 17.

Hindu patients and families

Adult Hindus are traditionally cremated. Young children and infants may be buried. Cremation or burial should take place as soon as possible, preferably within 24 hours.

There is no Hindu prohibition against organ donation, although individual families may find it unacceptable.

There is no Hindu prohibition against post mortems, although again some people find them unacceptable. Some families may be concerned that all the organs are returned to the body before cremation or burial.

Interpreter

The bereavement officer should find out from ward staff whether she will need an interpreter for the interview and arrange for one if necessary. People who speak little or no English are also most unlikely to be familiar with the bureaucratic regulations surrounding death in Britain and may need extra help and guidance.

Where possible a trained hospital interpreter should be used, since the discussion is likely to be both complex and emotionally charged. If none is available a reliable agency should be contacted to supply a suitable person. Brief the interpreter before the interview. The interpreter may also need to accompany the relatives to register the death and to help them with arrangements for the funeral and so on. The hospital should pay the interpreter for this time.

Jehovah's Witness patients and families

There are no special religious requirements for the disposal of the body.

There is no religious objection to organ donation or to post mortems.

Jewish patients and families

Burial normally takes place as soon as possible, usually within 24 hours, and arrangements should not be delayed for hospital or administrative convenience. In some areas registrars make special arrangements so that Orthodox Jews can register a death on a Saturday. If a person dies on the Sabbath (Saturday) or a religious holiday, the funeral will normally take place on Sunday or after the holiday.

Members of the family or the community may wish to sit with the body until it is removed from the hospital. A quiet room will be needed for this. More information and advice can be obtained from your local synagogue, or from the Jewish Memorial Council, Woburn House, Upper Woburn Place, London WC1 (071-387 3081) and the United Synagogue and Burial Society at the above address, (071-387 7891, 24 hour answerphone).

For Orthodox Jews a body must be buried, never cremated.

Orthodox Jews do not permit post mortems unless they are required by law.

Orthodox Jews do not permit any action which would mar or dishonour the body. Organ donation is therefore normally forbidden.

Marriage

People who are seriously ill and likely to die can make either a civil or a church marriage in hospital (see below). (See HM(71)42 Marriage (Registrar General's Licence) Act 1970.) People who wish to make a religious marriage and are not members of the Church of England or the Church in Wales should make a civil marriage as outlined below and organise any religious ceremony they wish as well.

Marriage – civil

An application for a civil marriage licence must be made in person to the superintendent registrar of the district in which the hospital is sited. Get his/her name from the local registrar. In an emergency the necessary information can be given to the registrar in the hospital immediately before the marriage ceremony.

The licence will only be granted if one of the couple is seriously ill, is not expected to recover, and cannot be moved to a place where marriages are normally conducted. A doctor responsible for the care of the dying patient should confirm these facts in writing to the superintendent registrar, stating also that the dying person is capable of understanding the nature of the marriage ceremony.

If either party has been married before, they must produce a copy of the death certificate of the spouse (if widowed) or a copy of the decree absolute (if divorced).

The marriage licence can be issued immediately. A fee will be charged.

The civil marriage ceremony can take place anywhere except in the hospital chapel. Two witnesses are needed who must both sign the marriage register. For further information and advice contact the Marriages Section, The General Register Office, St Catherine's House, 10 Kingsway, London WC2B 6JP (071-242 0262).

Marriage – Church of England or Church in Wales

In cases of grave emergency the Archbishop of Canterbury may grant a special licence for the marriage to be solemnised at any time or any place. However this licence is granted at his discretion and may not be granted if one or both of the parties has been divorced or if neither of the parties has been baptised into the Christian faith (though not necessarily the Church of England or Church in Wales). If the special licence is refused the couple should go through a civil marriage ceremony (see above). The marriage may be blessed straight afterwards by a chaplain, and the couple can exchange marriage vows if they wish.

To arrange a Church of England or Church in Wales wedding the chaplain or other responsible person should contact the Chief Clerk of the Faculty Office, 1 The Sanctuary, London SW1P 3JT (071-222-5381) open Monday to Friday 10am to 4pm, with clerks on call on the same number out of hours. The application for a special licence must be supported by the minister who has agreed to solemnise the marriage. A doctor responsible for the care of the dying patient must confirm in writing that the patient is seriously ill and is not expected to recover, cannot be moved, and is in full possession of his or her mental faculties. The hospital manager must give written permission for the marriage to take place on the premises.

In addition, one of the couple must provide a sworn affidavit stating the full names of the people to be married and their ages, giving the name of the person who has agreed to solemnise the marriage, and stating that neither party has been divorced. The affidavit may be sworn either before the local Church of England or Church in Wales minister or at the Faculty Office.

Medical cause of death certificate

Unless the death is to be referred to the coroner, relatives must take the medical cause of death certificate, signed by the doctor who verified the death, to the registrar's office to register the death.

It is extremely important that relatives who have come to the hospital to collect the certificate do not have to wait for the doctor to sign it or, worse still, have to come back to collect it later. The bereavement officer must ensure that all medical cause of death certificates have been signed by the appropriate doctors at least half an hour before relatives could arrive at the hospital on the day following the death.

She should speak to all new junior doctors during their induction course, explaining the importance of signing certificates promptly, and detailing how, where and when certificates should be signed.

Nevertheless, she may sometimes have to chase junior doctors who have failed to sign in time. To do this she must liaise closely with the switchboard and the medical staffing officer so that she has an up-to-date list of all the doctors working in the hospital, identified by specialty, with their bleep numbers, as well as the telephone numbers of all the consultants. This list must be revised regularly and at every intake of new junior doctors. She must also have a copy of each day's operating list in order to contact doctors before they go into theatre. If a certificate is not signed in time and the junior doctor responsible is unwilling to leave his duties the bereavement officer should contact his consultant about it.

The signing doctor must fill in the form in a way that will be acceptable to the registrar. A certificate that is vague, does not give a specific or possible cause of death, or is partially blank is not acceptable and the registrar will send relatives back to the hospital to get another. If there is any doubt or query the doctor should telephone the registrar.

The patient's doctor or the bereavement officer should tell the relatives at the interview what is written on the certificate and make sure that they understand it. A doctor should be called to speak to the relatives if necessary.

The officer must hand the certificate to the relatives in a sealed envelope. It is courteous to explain that she is legally required to seal the envelope and that this does not in any way imply lack of trust in them.

Mortuary

Inadequate procedures for the care and release of bodies from hospital mortuaries are a frequent cause of relatives' complaints.

The bereavement officer should ensure that all procedures are followed correctly, for example:

• The name bracelet must never be removed from the deceased person's wrist.

• Each body must have a name tag attached to the ankle or toe.

• The mortuary sheet must also be clearly labelled with the deceased person's name, age, religion, measurements and date and time of death, and whether there are any rings on the body.

• A mortuary register of bodies received should be carefully completed and available at all times. It should list the name of the deceased person, the date of death and the other details on the label mentioned above, the date the body was received into the mortuary, whether a post mortem was performed and for whom, to whom the body was released and the date of release. The person collecting the body and the hospital employee releasing it should both sign the mortuary register.

The officer is also responsible for ensuring that:

• Local funeral directors know when the mortuary is open for the collection of bodies and the correct procedures.

• Representatives of the funeral directors, the coroner, the police and anyone else are always accompanied in the mortuary by a member of the hospital staff.

• No one is allowed to remove the body without proof of identity and written authorisation. Funeral directors should produce a signed release slip (or authorisation slip) and/or a certificate for burial or cremation (green form) from the registrar's office. If there is any doubt, the body should not be released and the mortuary technician should contact the consultant pathologist for advice.

Mortuary chapel

The mortuary chapel should be adaptable to meet the needs of relatives of all religious faiths.

The bereavement officer, or another named person, must have overall responsibility for the upkeep and condition of the mortuary chapel and its approaches, and for the way that viewing is organised. She should inspect the facilities regularly and report any problems. A suitable checklist is included in Appendix H.

Muslim patients and families

Muslims are buried, not cremated. According to Islamic law and practice, Muslims must be buried as soon as possible, normally within 24 hours.

Very strict Muslims are likely to be completely against organ transplants, but some may consider them acceptable.

In Islam, the body of a Muslim is considered to belong to God, and, strictly speaking, no part of a dead body should be cut out or harmed. Post mortems are normally forbidden unless required for legal reasons. If a post mortem is required, the reasons for it must be explained clearly to the family.

Neonatal death

The death of a baby within 28 days after birth is known as a neonatal death.

The doctor who verifies the death should complete the special medical cause of death certificate. This should be given to the parents to take to the registrar's office. If the baby's birth has not already been registered, the parents can register the birth and death at the same time.

If the baby was born in one district and died in another, the death must be registered in the district in which it occurred. The parents can, if they wish, register the birth at the same time 'by declaration' – that is, they do not need to go and register the birth separately in the district in which the baby was born. They will get a birth certificate in the normal way. (If the parents wish they can register the birth separately. They do not have to register the birth before they can register the death.)

Tell the parents that they can ask for copies of the birth and death certificates and that they can have the baby's forenames entered on both.

If the doctor is unable to issue a certificate, or further investigation is considered necessary, the death will be reported to the coroner. If he decides to carry out a post mortem, the parents can appeal against this in the usual way to the high court, although this will delay the funeral.

If a post mortem is carried out by the hospital a doctor who knows the parents should explain and discuss the findings with them. Written consent must be obtained from the parents.

Although the hospital is not bound by law to pay for a funeral in the case of a neonatal death, some do. (For more information about organising funerals for very young babies see **Stillbirth**, page 50.) Parents who wish to organise the funeral themselves, and who receive income support, family credit or housing benefit, may be able to get help towards funeral expenses. (See **Funeral expenses – help with**, page 33.)

Parents should be told of the support offered by SANDS (the Stillbirth and Neonatal Death Society (see **Useful addresses**, page 75) and given copies of the SANDS leaflet for parents, *What has to be done*, and *The loss of your baby*, published by the Health Education Authority, Hamilton House, Mabledon Place, London WC1 (071-631 0930).

All bereavement officers who deal with bereaved parents of very young babies should refer to *Miscarriage, stillbirth and neonatal death: guidelines for professionals*, to be published by SANDS, January 1991.

No next of kin – registering the death

See **Acting for the next of kin,** page 16.

Porters

Porters are often the public's first point of contact with a hospital. It is therefore essential that they are trained to deal sympathetically with everyone they meet. Desk porters should be informed when bereaved relatives are due to arrive and, if possible, should escort them to the bereavement officer's room.

At nights and at weekends the front hall porter may hold the bereavement officer's appointments book, so that nursing staff can make appointments for relatives to see her.

Many porters who have to remove the bodies of deceased patients from the wards find it frightening and distressing. They need training and support in this area of their work.

Post mortem – coroner's

See **Coroner's post mortem,** page 22.

**Post mortem –
hospital**

Medical staff who wish to request a hospital post mortem for research or educational purposes should tell the bereavement officer before she sees the relatives. She should prepare them for the request and call the appropriate doctor or senior nurse who should come as soon as possible. Relatives should not be kept waiting. The doctor or senior nurse should offer to inform the relatives of the findings, either personally or through their GP.

Many people dislike the idea of a post mortem and may be reluctant to consent. Some people, for example Orthodox Jews and Muslims, may refuse consent for religious reasons (unless the post mortem is legally required by the coroner: see **Coroner's post mortem**, page 22.) The request for a post mortem must always be made sensitively. No one should ever be pressurised to agree to a post mortem against their will. Hospital post mortems sometimes delay funerals and relatives should be warned if this is likely to happen.

Relatives cannot legally consent to a hospital post mortem if the deceased person was known to have any objection or if the surviving spouse or any other known surviving relative objects.

If the relatives agree to a post mortem they must sign a consent form (see Appendix I). The bereavement officer should keep this in the deceased person's medical record which should be taken to the pathologist. Each consent form should be numbered and listed in a register of hospital post mortems (see Appendix J).

Sometimes relatives only agree to a hospital post mortem under certain conditions – for example, that they receive a full copy of the pathologist's report or that the post mortem is partial. No post mortem should be carried out where these conditions are unacceptable to or cannot be met by the hospital.

The only case in which a signed consent form is not required by law is that of a baby stillborn before 28 weeks gestation. Although consent is not legally required at present in such cases the parents should always be asked formally for their consent and no post mortem should be carried out if they refuse.

Property

The bereavement officer is responsible for any property at the hospital and for its safe handling and disposal.

A nurse should deliver all property from the ward and the ward safe to the officer at least an hour before the first relatives start to arrive in the morning. This will ensure that she has time to check and repack it if necessary. Relatives having to watch someone sorting through the property of the person they love is intolerable. Property awaiting collection by other relatives should be stored out of sight.

The bereavement officer should also collect any property belonging to a deceased patient from the hospital safe and sign the appropriate pages in the property book.

In some hospitals she collects the property from the wards herself. Talking to the nurses can provide useful information for the interview with the relatives.

Half empty bottles of squash, flowers, packets of biscuits and so on should not automatically be handed back to relatives but should be kept on the ward. Relatives should be asked if they want them. Sponges, flannels, toothbrushes and so on should be wrapped separately and marked so that relatives can choose whether they want to open them. Soiled clothes should be either wrapped separately and marked, or laundered and sent on later. Get well cards should be put in a marked envelope. Problems to do with the way property is prepared for handing over should be taken up with the nurse in charge of the ward.

The property should be given to the relatives in suitable bags, be strong enough to bear the weight of clothes and other items. The bags must have good handles, be able to close properly, and be discreet. Most people find today's standard NHS patients' property bags undignified and lacking in respect. If the relatives have a long journey ahead they should be offered a suitcase for the property. A stock of unclaimed suitcases should be kept for this purpose.

Many relatives find the experience of receiving property harrowing. Great tact and sensitivity are needed. Have the patient's property, money and valuables ready. Ask the relatives to check the money and valuables and to sign the indemnity form (see Appendix E). Then ask them if they wish to check the other property, but do not press them, and ask them to sign the property sheet.

In some hospitals relatives collect property from the nurses on the ward. Many people prefer receiving property from someone they already know. The bereavement officer should check that the nursing staff know the proper procedures.

The officer is not responsible for administering a patient's estate or for protecting any property not in her possession.

Property – no next of kin

If next of kin cannot be traced but a will is found, it should be sent to the executor or the solicitor named in the will.

Property – no next of kin and no will

If a patient dies with no known relatives and without a will (intestate) their estate belongs to the Crown.

If, after funeral expenses and so on, the net value of the remaining property, including money and valuables, is less than £250 (1989) it should be handed over to the hospital cashier. He should keep valuable property and money for at least six years, and other property for at least six months, in case someone claims them (Limitation Act 1980 S22).

The bereavement officer should send National Savings Certificates to the Director of the National Savings Bank, Savings Certificate Division, Durham; National Savings Books to the Director of the National Savings Bank, Glasgow GS8 1SB; cheque books or pass books to the appropriate banks or building societies, and pension books to the Department of Social Security. Enclose with each an explanation of how they came to be held by the hospital and what has been done to the deceased person's next of kin. (These organisations should have been contacted at an earlier stage when trying to trace the next of kin: see **Tracing the next of kin**, page 53.

If, after funeral expenses and so on, the net value of the remaining property is more than £250 (1989) a finance officer should contact the Treasury Solicitor, Queen Anne's Chambers, 28 Broadway, London SW1H 9JS (071-210 3000 or 071-210 3094). The Treasury Solicitor will need to know the full name and marital status of the deceased person, the date and place of death, the date of admission to hospital and the address from which they entered hospital. He will attempt to trace the next of kin. If unsuccessful he will administer the balance of the estate and retain it for 30 years.

If the total value of the person's estate is less than £500 net and there are also personal effects which have no obvious saleable value, the bereavement officer or hospital manager may dispose of these as they see fit after six months. (See also *The estates of persons dying without known kin and intestate*, 1986, from the Treasury Solicitor.)

Property – uncollected

If the next of kin do not come to collect the property it should be sent to them by registered post. Enclose an indemnity form and a property sheet for the recipient to sign, with a stamped addressed envelope and a covering letter.

Property – value over £5,000

Normally, the bereavement officer should hand over any money a deceased patient brought into hospital to the relatives and ask them to sign an indemnity form.

However, if the total value of the property exceeds £5,000, the patient's executor must produce a grant of probate (or letters of administration if there is no will) before the hospital can hand the money over.

Publicity

In certain circumstances a death can attract media attention: for example, if organs are donated, if the person is a celebrity, or if there is an inquest. It is most important that the strictest confidentiality is maintained unless the next of kin wishes otherwise. The hospital should appoint one person to answer all press and other enquiries and to issue press statements. Contact the regional press officer for advice if necessary. (See also **Suggested reading**, page 73.)

Registering the death

The death must be registered within five days at the office of the registrar of births and deaths in whose district the hospital stands.

The death must be registered in person – that is, not by letter or telephone, by someone who is qualified to be an informant under the Births and Deaths Registration Act 1953. This should normally be a relative. If there are no relatives or they are too old or frail to get to the register office, the death can be registered by anyone who was present at the death, by the bereavement officer (see **Acting for the next of kin**, page 16), or by the person arranging the funeral (but *not* by the funeral director). If there are any questions about any aspects of registering the death, the relatives or the bereavement officer should contact the registrar as soon as possible for advice.

The person who registers the death must take the medical cause of death certificate, signed by the appropriate doctor, from the hospital to the registrar. If possible, he or she should also take the following information.

- The deceased person's full name including surname (and the maiden name of a married woman or widow).

- The deceased person's usual address, (the hospital, if they were a long-stay patient).

- Their date and place of birth (on their birth certificate if available).

- Their occupation (and the name and occupation of the deceased person's husband if she was a married woman or a widow).

- The date of birth of the deceased person's surviving husband or wife (if any).

- Whether the deceased person received a state pension or benefit.

The interview with the registrar is usually straightforward. The registrar will give the relatives two forms:

* A death certificate (certificate of registration of death) which is an exact and certified copy of the entry in the register. This can be taken to the Department of Social Security to apply for help with funeral expenses and widow's benefit if appropriate. Relatives will probably also need certified copies of the death certificate for personal business – for example, for banks, building societies, insurance companies, and so on. These can be obtained for £2 each at or shortly after the time of registration. When the register is full (usually after two to three months) it is sent to the superintendent registrar of the district who will supply certified copies of the entry for £5 each (1989 prices). Contact the registrar for the superintendent registrar's name and address.

* A certificate for burial or cremation (green form). This permits the body to be buried or an application for cremation to be made. It should be given to the funeral director.

Release slip

Also known as an authorisation slip, it is a form authorising the hospital mortuary staff to release the body. It is given to the relatives by the bereavement officer for them to sign and give to the funeral director. She signs this herself if she arranges the funeral.

Repatriating the bodies of nationals of other countries

Families with strong links in other countries may wish to send the body of a deceased relative home for burial or cremation.

The bereavement officer should advise them to find a funeral director with extensive experience in this area as the necessary steps are very complicated. If no suitable funeral director can be found, the family should contact an appropriate airline for help and advice (see Appendix K).

Sikh patients and families

Sikhs are normally cremated, not buried. The cremation takes place as soon as possible, usually within 24 hours of the death.

A stillborn baby, or a baby who dies within a few days of birth, may be buried.

There is no religious prohibition against organ donation.

There is no religious prohibition against post mortems, but it is normally important that cremation takes place as soon as possible.

Stillbirth

All births, including stillbirths, must be registered (Births and Deaths Registration Act 1926).

The only exception to this is babies born dead before 28 weeks gestation. In the case of these babies, no legal registration of the birth or death is necessary at present. Although these babies have no legal existence, hospitals increasingly recognise the importance of helping the parents and other family members to grieve formally and to organise or participate in a funeral in the normal way.

The birth of a stillborn baby born after 28 weeks gestation must be registered at the registrar's office within three months. The doctor or midwife who attended the delivery gives the parents a medical certificate of stillbirth to take to the registrar. The registrar will also need to know the mother's name, usual address, occupation, and date and place of birth; the father's name (if the parents are married), his usual address, occupation, and date and place of birth; and the date and time of the baby's delivery. If the parents are not married the situation is complex. Contact the registrar before going to the register office.

The registrar will give the parents:

* A certificate of registration of stillbirth. It is important to tell the parents that they can ask for the baby's forenames to be entered in the register and on the certificate. Copies of the stillbirth certificate itself can be obtained after two or three months from the Registrar General of Births, Deaths and Marriages, St Catherine's House, 10 Kingsway, London WC2 (071-242 0262) for a fee of £5.

* A certificate for burial or cremation (white form). This should be given to the funeral director, or, if the hospital is arranging the funeral, to the administrator.

If the body of a stillborn baby is to be cremated, the doctor who verified the death must fill in a cremation form for a stillborn child (form H). No second medical certificate is needed. It is illegal to collect a fee for the doctor who signs the cremation form.

If a post mortem is to be carried out, a signed consent form must be obtained in the usual way.

A stillborn baby of over 28 weeks gestation must, by law, be formally buried or cremated. Although there is no legal requirement to formally bury or cremate a stillborn baby born before 28 weeks gestation many parents still wish this to be done and should be given all the help they need.

If the parents do not wish to organise the funeral themselves, the hospital can arrange it through a local funeral director with whom they have a contract. Unless the parents prefer a cremation the baby will be buried. The parents should be given the opportunity to participate in the funeral as much as they wish and should contact the funeral director to discuss this as soon as they feel able. The hospital should not charge the parents for the funeral, although the parents may have to pay the funeral director for things not covered in the hospital contract (see HN(76)18 and DS 211/75).

When discussing the decision about a funeral with the parents it is important to explain to them what a funeral organised by the hospital will be like and how it is likely to differ from a private funeral. (The term contract funeral sounds uncaring to lay ears and should not be used when talking to parents.) For example, the grave may contain the coffins of several babies and it may be some time before the grave is finally sealed; the parents cannot normally put up any kind of memorial of their own, though some cemeteries allow a general memorial stone on which the baby's name can be written. The bereavement officer should find out in advance from the contract funeral director what local arrangements are and how much flexibility there is.

The hospital's contract with the funeral director should specify that parents will be able to participate in a contract funeral and give details. The bereavement officer must ensure that the funeral director with whom the hospital has a contract is sensitive to the needs of bereaved parents and gives a high standard of flexible service. She should attend contract funerals regularly to monitor the quality of service.

Parents who wish to organise the funeral themselves and who receive income support, family credit or housing benefit may be able to get help towards funeral expenses. (see **Funeral expenses – help with**, page 33.)

Parents should be told of the support offered by SANDS (the Stillbirth and Neonatal Death Society – see **Useful addresses**, page 75) and given copies of the SANDS leaflet for parents, *What has to be done*, and *The loss of your baby*, published by the Health Education Authority, Hamilton House, Mabledon Place, London WC1 (071-631 0930).

All bereavement officers who deal with parents of stillborn babies should refer to *Miscarriage, stillbirth and neonatal death: guidelines for professionals*, to be published by SANDS, January 1991.

Tracing the next of kin

The bereavement officer should examine the patient's case notes and possessions and write to anyone who might be related to inform them of the death and try to trace the next of kin. Keep a record of all letters and telephone calls to show what has been done. Contact the police for help. Also write to the issuing organisations of any documents such as cheque and building society books. Also, local social services offices, housing departments, possibly local churches and religious organisations, the family practitioner committee and other local hospital medical records departments. And, if appropriate, embassies and high commissions.

If a relative is found, invite him or her to register the death (if this has not been done), and to arrange the funeral and wind up the estate. Any official documents should be sent by registered post. (See also **Acting for the next of kin**, page 16.)

Training – for the bereavement officer

All bereavement officers should receive training in basic communication and counselling skills and in dealing with difficult situations when they are first appointed. They should also have a regular opportunity to meet, formally or informally, with other people doing the same job to talk about the stresses involved and to share solutions to particular problems.

Training – for other staff

The bereavement officer is responsible for ensuring that all hospital staff who deal with bereaved relatives understand her role, know how to contact her and when she is available, and can tell relatives how to contact her. They also need a good general idea of what relatives have to do after a death, in case they are asked.

She should meet all new nursing, medical, administrative, reception and portering staff, either singly or during induction or other training, to provide information about her role and theirs in helping relatives cope with the administrative and legal procedures surrounding death.

Viewing the body

All relatives should be offered the opportunity to view the body of the deceased person in the viewing chapel. This offer should be made by the nurses on the ward and also, if appropriate, by the bereavement officer when she sees the relatives.

The officer is responsible for making sure that there is a clear and easy procedure for the relatives to arrange viewing, both through the nursing staff on the ward and through her, and that all the nurses can explain this to relatives and know what to do if relatives want to view. (See also **Mortuary chapel**, page 40.)

She is also responsible for ensuring that the porters concerned lay the body out acceptably in the mortuary chapel and remove it promptly when relatives have left. The cloth over the body should be clean and fresh.

A nurse from the patient's ward should normally accompany all relatives to the mortuary chapel. Before they go in, she should check that the body is well laid out and that the chapel is clean and tidy. The relatives may wish for a chaplain to visit the chapel with them. The bereavement officer or a nurse should arrange this.

Volunteers

If a relative is alone and confused or very distressed the bereavement officer should, where possible, ask if they would like a volunteer to go with them to register the death.

In some hospitals volunteers have organised a special 'companionship' service which is offered to bereaved relatives who live alone and would like support and companionship at home in the first few days after the death.

The officer should always brief the volunteer about the circumstances and emotional state of the relative.

Will

If a will has been handed over to the bereavement officer for safe keeping or is found among the patient's possessions, she must give or send it either to the person named in the will as the executor, or to the patient's solicitor (not to any other relatives) as soon as possible after the patient's death. She may open the will to find out the name and address of the executor. It is a criminal offence to destroy a will.

Will – making one in hospital

A patient who wishes to make a will in hospital should normally use their own solicitor. If they do not have one, or the solicitor is far away, the bereavement officer should provide a list of local solicitors and offer to contact whoever the patient chooses. Explain to the patient that they will have to pay the solicitor in the normal way. A list should be kept of local solicitors who are prepared to come to the hospital even outside normal working hours if needed.

If there is not enough time to contact a solicitor the bereavement officer can help the patient to make a will. She should keep a stock of standard will forms (Wills No 6, available from Oyez Stationery Ltd, 49 Bedford Row, London WC1R 4LS (071-242 7132).

Under the Wills Act 1837, a will is only valid if it is in writing, signed, dated, and witnessed by two people who are not beneficiaries or related to beneficiaries. The witnesses must both see the patient signing the will. They should preferably both be senior managers. Nurses should not normally act as witnesses in case the patient wants to leave some money to the hospital in which case they could apparently be considered to have influenced the decision. If the will is contested the witnesses may have to appear in court.

In addition:

the patient must be of sound mind. If there is any doubt about this or if it seems likely that the will may be contested, a doctor should witness the will, and should record his views on the patient's ability to make a will in the medical notes;

every page of the will and any amendments or alterations must be initialled by the patient and both witnesses.

Sample leaflet for nurses to give relatives when a patient has died

UNIVERSITY COLLEGE HOSPITAL

INFORMATION AND ADVICE FOR BEREAVED
RELATIVES AND FRIENDS

Please accept the sympathy of the hospital
staff on your recent bereavement. We hope
you will find this guide helpful.

This leaflet outlines the things you will need to do when somebody has died, and gives information about people who can help.

PEOPLE WHO CAN HELP

Nursing staff
Do remember that the nursing staff on the ward will be pleased to answer any queries you may have, or discuss any problems.

Administration
Ms Meenu Daryanani and Ms Anna Gillard are the Patients' Welfare Officers in the Administration Office, close to the Gower Street entrance hall of the hospital. They will help you with the administrative details, and are pleased to give you advice and help. The Administration Office is on the 1st floor of the hospital. It is open from 10.00am to 4.30pm. If you wish to be seen at a specific time, please contact the Administration Office to arrange a firm appointment.

Tel: 071-387 9300 ext 8076

Chaplains
The Church of England and Roman Catholic chaplains are usually in the hospital and easily available to help you. There are also Free Church and Jewish chaplains. The nursing staff can contact them and ministers of other faiths for you.

The Chapel of All Saints in the basement of the Rockefeller Nurses Home is open at all times for prayer and meditation. The nursing staff will be able to show you how to find it.

Funeral director
A list of local funeral directors is available from the Administration Office. You may find it helpful to contact them as soon as possible, for example before you have registered the death. They can often advise you on what to do next.

THE CHAPEL OF REST

There is a chapel of rest at the hospital where you can pay your respects. The ward staff or the Administration Department can arrange this for you.

THINGS YOU NEED TO DO

Collecting the death certificate and personal effects
You will need to collect the death certificate from Ms Daryanani or Ms Gillard in the Administration Office on the 1st floor of the hospital. It is open from 10.00am to 4.30pm.

When you collect the death certificate you will also be given any clothing and personal effects. You may like to bring a small case or bag for these.

Some sudden or unexpected deaths have to be reported to the coroner who will then issue the death certificate. He may require a legal post mortem. Ms Daryanani or Ms Gillard in the Administration Office will explain the procedure to you and will put you in touch with the coroner's office. The coroner's officer can help you sort out any problems.

The coroner's office is situated behind St Pancras Hospital, the entrance is in Camley Street.

Opening hours: Monday to Friday 8.30am–4pm
                 Saturday   8.30am–12 noon

Tel: 071-387 4884

Post mortem

The doctor may ask for permission to carry out a post mortem examination at the hospital. Post mortems can sometimes help doctors to understand more about a disease. Hospital post mortems are not compulsory and you do not have to agree if you do not wish. You can ask for a limited post mortem, you can also ask to be told the results.

Registering a death

All deaths at University College Hospital must be registered at the Camden Registrar's Office.

Camden Town Hall (Argyll Street entrance)
Euston Road
London NW1 2RU

Tel: 071-278 4444

The office is open from 9.30am to 12.30pm and from 2.00pm to 4.00pm on Monday to Friday and from 9.00am to 11.30am on Saturdays.

A close relative must register the death within 5 days. You will need to take the following information about the person who has died:

1. The death certificate
2. Full name (and maiden name if married)
3. Date and place of birth
4. Occupation (and husband's occupation for a married woman)
5. Usual address.
6. Details of any state pension.
7. Date of birth of surviving spouse (if any).

If you have it, you must give the medical card of the person who has died to the Registrar. The Registrar will give you a green form for the DSS. You can get copies of the death certificate for £2.00 each. You may need these for a bank or insurance company.

ORGANISATIONS OFFERING HELP

The organisations listed below offer advice, counselling and help to those who have been bereaved.

Camden Bereavement Service
Camden Council of Social Service
25/31 Tavistock Place
London WC1H 9SE

Tel: 071-388 2071

Westminster Bereavement Service
42 Warwick Avenue
London W9 2PT

Tel: 071-289 6597

Cruse (for widows, widowers and their children)
126 Sheen Road
Richmond Road
Surrey TW9 1UR

Tel: 081-940 4818/9047

The Compassionate Friends (for bereaved parents)
50 Woodwaye
Watford
Hertfordshire WD1 4NW

Tel: 0923 24279

The Foundation for the Study of Infant Deaths
(Cot Deaths)
14 Belgrave Square
London SW1

Tel: 071-235 1721/0965

Hospital register of deaths (1) chronological

Register number	Date of death	Name	Sex	Age	Ward	Coroner's case	Post mortem in hospital (H) or public (P) mortuary	Address of deceased	Religion

Hospital register of deaths (2)
in alphabetical order of surname

Name	Date admitted	Date died	Hospital district number	Ward	Consecutive number of hospital register of death

Release slip to permit the release of a body from the hospital mortuary

BLOOMSBURY HEALTH AUTHORITY
RELEASE SLIP

Date_____

The Bereavement Officer
Middlesex Hospital

Please Allow Messrs _____

Funeral Directors of, _____

_____ Tel: _____

To remove the body of the late _____

Signed _____

Name of relative or executor in block letters _____

_____

Address _____

_____

Tel: _____

Are you the nearest surviving relative or the executor? __

If not, please state the capacity in which you sign this

form _____

_____

Removal times: Monday to Friday 9.00am to 12.30pm
1.30pm to 3.30pm

NO REMOVALS CAN TAKE PLACE AFTER 3.15 PM
Bereavement Officer's Office. Tel: _____

Indemnity form

BLOOMSBURY HEALTH AUTHORITY
FORM OF INDEMNITY

To: Bereavement Officer _____ From: _____
Middlesex Hospital
Mortimer Street
Address: _____

London W1

_____

_____

Patient's name _____ Patient's hospital no _____

IN CONSIDERATION of your paying to me the sum of £ _____and/or your handing over to me the property listed below, being the assets now in your hands of the estate of the above-named deceased I HEREBY UNDER-TAKE to idemnify you and keep you idemnified against all actions, proceedings, claims or demands whatsoever which may be taken or made against you by any person claiming to be interested in the estate of the above-named deceased or otherwise and against any costs or expenses whatsoever which may be incurred or become payable in respect thereof.

LIST OF PROPERTY HANDED OVER

_____

_____

_____

_____

_____

Witness:

Name _____Signed_____

Address _____

Relationship to patient _____

Occupation _____Date _____

Funeral expenses form

BLOOMSBURY HEALTH AUTHORITY
FUNERAL EXPENSES

To: <u>Unit General Manager</u> Date: _____

The late _____ Age: _____

Address _____

died _____ Religion: _____

With reference to this patient I have been asked to authorise the payment by the hospital of:

    A.   The funeral expenses or

    B.   The cost of transporting the coffin to the patient's home, which is outside the local area.

A. FUNERAL EXPENSES

I confirm that:

1. The deceased patient's relatives cannot be traced.
2. The relatives are traceable but refuse to arrange for burial.
3. The relatives are able/unable to obtain a death grant and/but cannot afford to arrange for burial.

B. TRANSPORT EXPENSES

I confirm that the patient was admitted to the

_____ Hospital because:

1. The treatment required was not available nearer home.
2. There was no vacancy in a hospital nearer to his home.

Signed: _____

Date: _____

*Please delete those paragraphs which do not apply

Standard letter to inform GPs of a patient's death

BLOOMSBURY HEALTH AUTHORITY

Middlesex Hospital, Mortimer Street, London W1

Telephone:

NOTE TO GENERAL MEDICAL PRACTITIONER

Date: _____

To: Dr _____

      _____

      _____

      _____

Dear Dr

Recent Death of Patient

I regret to inform you that your patient _____

died in the Middlesex Hospital on _____

The cause of death was _____

_____

Further details will follow shortly in the discharge

summary.

Yours sincerely

_____ (Signature)

(Name in block capitals)

Checklist for monitoring the

a. This section concerns features which should be monitored on a weekly/monthly basis perhaps with the domestic service manager, head porter, mortuary attendant and senior nurse.

Features to be checked	Yes/No	Comments and acceptability: (For instance, would this do for *you* and *your* relatives?)
Relatives' access route Are the corridors, passageways and steps clean and free of litter? Are the corridors walls painted, the paint not dingy or peeling and the walls not covered with graffiti? *Chapel* Are the walls, windows and floors clean? How often are they cleaned? Does this need to be altered? Are the chapel, walls, ceilings, doors well painted and the paintwork not chipped or flaking? Are the colours suitable? If fresh flowers are provided, are they changed regularly? If silk or artificial, are they clean? Are the chairs suitable, comfortable and clean? Is the atmosphere disturbed by noise of equipment or people outside? Are there unpleasant smells, possibly from refuse outside or dead flowers in the chapel? Is the cover used for the body changed and cleaned daily? Are there sufficient covers and are they to hand? Is it suitable for all creeds and denominations?		

state of the mortuary chapel

b. This section concerns features which should be considered but may require additional work and money to make necessary improvements.

Features to be checked	Yes/No	Comments and acceptability: (For instance, would this do for *you* and *your* relatives?)
Location: are there pieces of machinery or items of equipment stored close to the chapel? Do they enhance the approach? If not, do they need to be kept there or can they be relocated and stored elsewhere? Is there wheelchair access to the chapel either by the usual route or by an alternative route? Is this signposted? Has a feasibility study looked at this? Is there an appropriate sitting-room where relatives can talk to a nurse or a chaplain which is adjacent to or near the chapel? Can privacy be guaranteed? Are there viewing rooms available for relatives of non-Christian or non-religious patients? What alternative arrangements can be made to meet their needs?		

Post mortem consent form

Bloomsbury Health Authority Form of consent for post mortem examination	Hospital no: Surname: First Names: Date of Birth: Sex:

To the MEDICAL STAFF and BLOOMSBURY HEALTH
AUTHORITY

I _____

of _____

as next of kin, hereby consent to a post mortem

examination, including the removal of tissue under

Section 1 of the Human Tissue Act 1961, being carried

out on the body of the late _____

of _____

_____

Signed: _____ Relationship to deceased: _____

Please attach this form to the notes of the inpatient
period to which it refers.

Register of post mortems

Name of Deceased	Date of death	Date received in mortuary	Coroner's post mortem	Post mortem in public mortuary	Post mortem for research	Death certificate Issued by GP	Date of Release	To whom

Total number of post mortems:

Total number of deaths:

Documents required for the repatriation of the bodies of deceased nationals

REPATRIATION OF DECEASED NATIONAL

The following documents are required. All the procedures except registering the death are usually dealt with by the funeral director. If the funeral director cannot help, contact the appropriate airline for advice and help.

Death certificate issued by the registrar as normal.

The registrar will also supply form 104 which should be taken or sent to the coroner who will issue an out of England authority to allow the body to be moved out of the country.

Certificate of embalming All bodies must be embalmed to comply with international airline regulations, and, in many cases, national public health regulations.

Certificate of freedom of infection Usually signed by the medical officer of environmental health.

The funeral director should arrange any other essential procedures, and issue a declaration stating that all the requirements have been fulfilled and giving the flight details and details of the person collecting the body in the home country.

Suggested reading

Caring for dying patients of different faiths. Julia Neuberger, Lisa Sainsbury Foundation, 1987.

Caring for Hindus and their families: religious aspects of care. Alix Henley, National Extension College, 1983.

Caring for Muslims and their families: religious aspects of care. Alix Henley, National Extension College, 1983.

Caring for Sikhs and their families: religious aspects of care. Alix Henley, National Extension College, 1983.

Good practice in hospital care for dying patients. Project paper no. 61. Alix Henley, King Edward's Hospital Fund for London, 1988.

Health Service Commissioner: selected investigations. HMSO, London (issued four times a year).

Health service public relations: a guide to good practice. Edited by Roger Silver, King Edward's Hospital Fund for London, 1985.

Matters of death and life. Project paper no 77. Anthony Wright, Jennifer Cousins and Janet Upward, King Edward's Hospital Fund for London, 1988.

Miscarriage, stillbirth and neonatal death: guidelines for professionals. Stillbirth and Neonatal Death Society (SANDS) to be published January 1991.

Patients' property, income and allowances. HFM/CIPFA, London, 1987.

Unexpected infant deaths: guidelines for accident and emergency departments. Foundation for the Study of Infant Deaths, London, 1981.

Bereavement officers should also have copies of the following circulars. They are available from libraries such as the King's Fund Centre Library and from the Department of Health Stores, Health Publications Unit, No 2 Site, Manchester Road, Heywood, Lancashire OL10 2PZ.

DEPARTMENT OF HEALTH CIRCULARS

HM(71)42:	The marriage (Registrar General's Licence) Act 1970: death bed marriages
HM(72)41:	Patients dying in hospital

HSC(IS)156: ·	Guidance circular to NHS Authorities Human Tissue Act 1961 (1975)
HN(76)18:	Funerals for stillborn babies
HC(77)28:	Removal of tissue at post mortem examination: human tissue act 1961
HN(85)31:	Patients dying in hospital
HC(88)63:	Provision of donor organs for transplantation

HOME OFFICE CIRCULARS

No 65/1977:	Transplant surgery
No 169/1979:	Removal of organs for transplantation: code of practice
No 44/1983:	Removal of organs for transplantation: revised code of practice

Useful addresses

Compassionate Friends
(Support for bereaved
parents)
6 Denmark Street
Bristol BS1 5DQ
Tel: 0272-292 778

SATFA
(Support after termination for
abnormality)
29 Soho Square
London W1V 6JB
Tel: 071-439 6124

**Stillbirth and Neonatal
Death Society**
(Support for bereaved
parents)
28 Portland Place
London W1N 4DE
Tel: 071-436 5881

**Foundation for the Study of
Infant Deaths**
(Cot death research and
support)
14 Belgrave Square
London SW1
Tel: 071-235 1721/0965

CRUSE
(Organisation for the
widowed and their children)
Cruse House
126 Sheen House
Richmond
Surrey TW9 1UR
Tel: 081-940 4818/9047

Hospice Advisory Service
(Advice for staff, patients and
families)
St Christopher's Hospice
Lawrie Park Road
London SE26
Tel: 081-778 9252

Lisa Sainsbury Foundation
(Support, training and
publications for professionals
caring for dying people)
8–10 Crown Hill
Croydon
Surrey CR0 1RY
Tel: 081-686 9908

Terrence Higgins Trust
(Information, advice and help
on AIDS)
52–54 Gray's Inn Road
London WC1X 8JU
Tel: 071-831 0330 or 071-278
8745